BIBLE WORD SEARCH PUZZLES

EDWARD M. SEAGRIST

HALO PRESS

Contents

1

The Books of the Old Testament

```
L E V I T I C U S I S N E X M H I A M M I F C H
B E L C K O A P E T G E N E S I S N T N C W A N
E O U S B R V B A X F T K J R A C Y C S H I U O
H W P M O E Z A Q V O J B K P G N A D Y R T T J
A R I L A M R Q U A Q D T G O G G A H A O U U A
I H X I O S I E A H A K U K K A B A H S N D S R
M J R S H O I N H Q S R U S C H T C B R I I N X
E E C P N C I I C H R O N I C L E S J K C A E J
H H E F E N A R Y L S N J V A Z A O Y S L A O L
E E O F R W Z L S P A O E P C N D Q V G E U S E
N R Z E X E O W A P Y M R C R A E W S N S V M U
O M Y O R G H J M M R O E H C Z U T H I G J I M
R E Y H F S Z T O S V L M N A L N G I K H I J A
H E Z R A R R N S E S O I L T I E I U I U O I S
C R H E W I O E R E L S A W N A N S R I N H Q I
J J A U K R D B B T B F H R I O T A I A K U K N
O U F I E I S A A M B O H S O N L I H A Q M R E
N D N T P A E M B O U G A I Y A A A O P S O Z S
A G U C W M E L A O B N O I D H S H H N E T A S
S E D H F O P Z B O B O J A V U P C C T S Z E G
D S E D O S R Z T A E S O H S M L A S P H E R S
```

GENESIS	II CHRONICLES	DANIEL
EXODUS	EZRA	HOSEA
LEVITICUS	NEHEMIAH	JOEL
NUMBERS	ESTHER	AMOS
DEUTERONOMY	JOB	OBADIAH
JOSHUA	PSALMS	JONAH
JUDGES	PROVERBS	MICAH
RUTH	ECCLESIASTES	NAHUM
I SAMUEL	SONG OF SOLOMON	HABAKKUK
II SAMUEL	ISAIAH	ZEPHANIAH
I KINGS	JEREMIAH	HAGGAI
II KINGS	LAMENTATIONS	ZECHARIAH
I CHRONICLES	EZEKIEL	MALACHI

2
Old Testament Themes

```
E N S G N I R E D N A W S S E N R E D L I W D C
R S S E N T E G E E R K I N G N I P R I N O O O
P A P I R Y S U F F F E R I G N R A A M M R D N
R M J R M A R H E R E E S T A A I D A O A O E Q
O U U L A S C O A L E A R S I S U N D G N L E U
B E D A N A C L T D O M I S E J A S N G S E V E
L L A W S M E L A S U R E J G N I D L I U B E R
E S H R R M R A N I I J R E R W I E I N G D L I
M A S E E U M A D L T H D A D A V L V E N E E N
O U G S A E E W D Y B N D N A E O T O B I F B G
F L R T S L E E E U N E E N A H R I R H N F E C
S A E A O L E D L G L G V D A L L N P N O E V A
U N A T N A D E I I D H O L I Y E U A A S A O N
F D T E I N E E V V L B L L O V G A V M E T L A
F D N D N D R E E O I E E H E R O O R O S A E A
E A E I G S R L R M W D B G E E R R L S A N B N
R V S N D A A I A E E E E A G P G A P A I D I A
I I S I N U M V N R B R H N G I N A D S E O N K
N D V C A L S E C A R E T W A N D E R S D N A I
G A E T N A N M E R E H T F O N R U T E R O E N
D D E D I V I D D E T I N U M O D G N I K S G G
```

BEGINNINGS

CONQUERING CANAAN

DAVID'S REIGN

DEFEAT AND DELIVERANCE

DELIVERANCE

GENEALOGY AND HISTORY

GOD'S PROVIDENTIAL CARE

HOLINESS

ISRAEL AND JUDAH

JUDAH'S GREATNESS

KINGDOM UNITED, DIVIDED

KINSMAN REDEEMER

LAW RESTATED

MAN'S REASONING

PRAISE

PROBLEM OF SUFFERING

REBUILDING JERUSALEM'S WALL

RETURN OF THE REMNANT

SAMUEL, SAUL, AND DAVID

THE BELOVED

WILDERNESS WANDERINGS

WISDOM

3
The Creation Story

```
A T F C L U F T I U R F C R E A T U R E S
W S E L A I D E T A E R C D S L I M A G E
O E M D G T G I L F M S E E D W R S A A G
L R A O O O T H I T A N T O G O A T S L D
F M L G O D D L T E N A M I R F E S I S E
I A E F D E E S E R R I W O M A Y A D E L
R G W O M A N E A H N N A W R R E E L V W
M G N T C R E E P I N G T H I N G B U E O
A S A I O T V U O S D B E A T G I H O N N
M E S R N H E N N K L D R L H R G N S D K
E A R I D N N G T I F E S E L A O F G A I
N S A P E E I O R N I L E S H S L E N Y T
T O E S V S N G E D S L D P I S D I I S S
H N Y A E R G O E T H I O P I A N T V B U
I S E D S R A T S B M U L T I P L Y I A D
L H I D D E K E L L E M T H G I N R L S H
```

ADAM	EDEN	GRASS	PISON
AFTER HIS KIND	ETHIOPIA	HAVILAH	REST
ASSYRIA	EUPHRATES	HEAVEN	RIB
BDELLIUM	EVE	HERB	SEAS
BEASTS	EVENING	HIDDEKEL	SEASONS
BEGINNING	FEMALE	IMAGE	SEED
CATTLE	FIRMAMENT	KNOWLEDGE	SEVEN DAYS
CREATED	FISH	LIFE	SIGNS
CREATURES	FOWL	LIGHT	SPIRIT OF GOD
CREEPING THING	FRUITFUL	LIVING SOUL	STARS
DAY	GARDEN	MAN	TREES
DEEP SLEEP	GIHON	MALE	WATERS
DOMINION	GOD SAID	MORNING	WHALES
DUST	GOLD	MULTIPLY	WOMAN
EARTH	GOOD	NIGHT	YEARS

4
Animals of the Bible

```
E N I W S C O T U S B
L O F O A S P A N D E
U I Z L K L W I I R A
M L F P E E H S C I R
B F O X P M E T O B G
M O I Y E A L R R U N
G Q S S T C E S N I L
O O A S H P S E E A S
A E D B T O T L M A N
T H U I O A T B M A A
V L L Z W T P L R H P
L E I F A Y E K N O D
S T L C F M Q A X R D
R O E L U A X E Z S A
W I G S D R A P O E L
```

BEAR	DOG	LAMB	REPTILES
BIRDS	DONKEY	LEOPARD	ROE
BULL	FISH	LION	SHEEP
CALF	FOX	MULE	SWINE
CAMEL	GOAT	OX	UNICORN
CATTLE	INSECTS	RAM	WOLF

5

Fowls of the Air

```
L E A D B P I G E O N N O C L A F E S
A K C O C A E P V K C O C O U A X S P
P W O V O R T U R T L E H R R C Z L A
W A R E A O L O K E I E J M E A K W R
I H N C S T T W L P N X P O B D N O R
N N O P U S A G O S S I F R A G E F O
G R R R Q H A E P E L I C A N K V L W
T E E W T E K L S E L A W N I O A D G
Y T H H K N I W S D O T G T C O R E F
I T G R E A T O W L O S T R I C H I H
L I A Z U R E Z A Q E G D I R T R A P
N B U Q P C R A N E Y S W A L L O W M
```

BAT	FOWLS	NIGHT HAWK	QUAIL
BITTERN	GLEDE	OSPREY	RAVEN
COCK	GREAT OWL	OSSIFRAGE	SPARROW
CORMORANT	HAWK	OSTRICH	STORK
CRANE	HEN	OWL	SWALLOW
CUCKOO	HERON	PARTRIDGE	SWAN
DOVE	KITE	PEACOCK	TURTLE
EAGLE	LAPWING	PELICAN	VULTURE
FALCON	LITTLE OWL	PIGEON	

6

Insects and Reptiles

```
C H A M E L E O N A T S U C O L P B
W O R M C O C K A T R I C E S C A D
T N E P R E S Y R E I F G N I Y L F
N E F F K N V G P M G A A S H L M J
A D R A Z I L P S G R I S E O F E T
S C O R P I O N L N L O M P R T R O
O H G E P H B E E A O S W Q N N W R
R T R S S T E L K T R G P H E E O T
H O R S E L E A C H U E A I T P R O
V M A G G O T H A W O C D R D R M I
Y R F L E A L W T Z Z I L D D E A S
G U M C A T E R P I L L A R A S R E
```

ADDER	FLY	MOTH
ANT	FLYING FIERY SERPENT	PALMER-WORM
ASP	FROG	SCORPION
BEE	GNAT	SERPENT
BEETLE	GRASSHOPPER	SNAIL
CATERPILLAR	HORNET	SPIDER
CHAMELEON	HORSELEACH	TORTOISE
COCKATRICE	LICE	VIPER
DRAGON	LIZARD	WORM
EARTHWORM	LOCUST	
FLEA	MAGGOT	

7
Trees in the Bible

```
M Y R T L E L P P A
R E P I N U J O L W
T P A L M F C M M I
U R I F I E O E U L
N E O G D N R G L L
T D V A D O S R B O
S B R I M E H A E W
E O O A N P A N R K
H X C I T E T A R A
C Y P R E S S T Y O
S E V I L O U E A I
H S A L G U M M B L
O P N H A T T I H S
```

ALGUM

ALMOND

APPLE

ASH

BAY

BOX

CEDAR

CHESTNUT

CYPRESS

FIG

FIR

JUNIPER

MULBERRY

MUSTARD

MYRTLE

OAK

OIL

OLIVE

PALM

PINE

POMEGRANATE

SHITTAH

SYCAMORE

TEIL

VINE

WILLOW

8

Land Divisions in Palestine

```
M I J I L A T H P A N A D R
N I R U E B E N G I N S C A
O D A D D S M A N S S A D H
M U O R S E D N P R N M J C
M M M A H N A H S A B A U A
A E N O H P O Z A E A R D S
G A L I L E E N E L O I A S
M M A O N E B R A B M A H I
A D N I M A J N E B U E R M
D E C A P O L I S A E L A E
A I R Y S Y R E H S A L O O
A R A I T S I L I H P H I N
```

AMMON	GALILEE	PEREA
ASHER	IDUMEA	PHILISTIA
BASHAN	ISRAEL	PHOENICIA
BENJAMIN	ISSACHAR	REUBEN
CANAAN	JUDAH	SAMARIA
DAN	JUDEA	SIMEON
DECAPOLIS	LEBANON	SYRIA
EDOM	MANASSEH	ZEBULON
EPHRAIM	MOAB	
GAD	NAPHTALI	

9
Bible Deserts and Wilderness

```
V K W D P A R A N X A K Y Z S Z H
S A U B I D E G N E A T I T S I A
U D R S A N D Y S D A P I M A O N
C E H T O M E D E K H R Q O A E D
S S O D O M E S Z A N P G N V O Y
A H O D A R A B I A N N P A A A R
M J E K E T E A N G E L H L Z M D
A B E H S R E E B I H T S I N A I
D F T O A D E S E R E G T H O T M
E F H H U D C G I B E O N B U A E
O G S J E R U E L B A R R O N R S
```

ARABIAN	JERUEL	PARAN
BEERSHEBA	JUDEA	SHUR
BETHAVEN	KADESH	SIN
DAMASCUS	KEDEMOTH	SINAI
EDOM	MAON	ZIN
ENGEDI	NEAR GAZA	ZIPH
GIBEON	OF THE RED SEA	

10
"A" Words

```
T R A A N N A B A S A T
N S B A S H E R A A K H
A B A I T H A D E B A A
A L U R R H A P O A L N
M E A R A M E H A N A N
A M E B Y H A J U R B A
N A A B A R A K R A A H
O R A N A N A B R B L N
S A N N A T R A L A A A
R A H S A A B R A H A M
A B A R R B A S H A M A
G Q U A A B A N A B B H
A N M S B A G A Z A A C
H A A R S T N A T A S A
T A R T Y H H A H H H R
A H A C H J A A H A A D
B C H R A A N M M C N A
B A H Y C B N A G A A H
A N A A N A C A R A R S
G A B L N L A M A M R E
```

ABANA	ASA	CANA
ABBA	BAAL	CANAAN
ABRAHAM	BALAAM	GABBATHA
ACHAN	BAASHA	GAZA
ADAM	BACA	HAGAR
AHAB	BALAK	HAMAN
AHAZ	BARABBAS	HANNAH
ANNA	BARAK	HARAN
ANNAS	BARNABAS	JABAL
ARAM	BASHAN	LABAN
		MAACAH
		MARA
		MARAH
		MARTHA
		NAAMAN
		NATHAN
		PARAN
		RAHAB
		RAMAH
		SARAH
		SATAN
		SHADRACH
		SHAMGAR
		TABBATH
		TAMAR

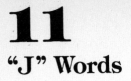

11
"J" Words

```
J J X S H P W J U D E V I F C H R A A
O J E R E M I A H G N M J B J A S O N
H E O T P V D Q E T J O A S H I Y K N
A J O S H Y H H J O E G B D Z D A B A
N J Q S U E L N C Y H A R T W I X K O
A E A V X S R H Y B O I N U F D C M J
N H P E U R E O E J S B A C K E S N E
T U W I L B L J D Z H S E M A J J M S
R C H U E O L G F M A O B O R E J Q A
X A P D O Y H C B E P T M A H T O J E
W L E E J O S I A H H P J E Z E B E L
Q F S K I Z N A H T A N O J V Q M T P
G R O W G U R J U S T U S O Y T E H C
L W J E M I M A X P H A H A D U J R A
A Z K D F B S C M I D C U V J L O O N
B Y D P J E H O V A H J A K E F N P D
U Q M T U D T B B S V X C J U D A S Y
J E H O I A K I M P A L J Z Q U H F R
```

JACOB	JEROBOAM	JOHN
JAEL	JESUS	JONAH
JAMES	JETHER	JONATHAN
JASON	JETHRO	JOSEPH
JEDIDIAH	JEZEBEL	JOSHUA
JEHOIAKIM	JOAB	JOSIAH
JEHOSHAPHAT	JOANNA	JOTHAM
JEHOVAH	JOASH	JUBAL
JEHU	JOB	JUDAH
JEHUCAL	JOCHEBED	JUDAS
JEMIMA	JOEL	JUDE
JEREMIAH	JOHANAN	JUSTUS

12
Women of the Bible

```
H A N I D Z Y M S A R O H A R U T E K X
A A V W E L I S A B E T H I T H S A V D
N U E T L R M S P R I S C I L L A R E A
H A P L I Z O H P P Y H P E E S Q B M E
A T H A L I A H H A T M B H E H O E O L
B L M M A R N O I U T E A N A R C A L I
E O K J H I E S R M Z T A G A A N Y A A
H H R O A N N A A E E T A H D N R E S G
S A D P R G C R J F H R S N A A B E R I
H A N A A H T A M A R T A A M E L A A B
T D H N E H H H A S H C A B O E M E M A
A A C L A N A D R I E L L H E A V B N A
B A R B A H T I B A T Z P H R E H T S E
Z I P P O R A H A K E B E R B I L H A H
```

ABIGAIL	EVE	PRISCILLA
ACHSAH	HAGAR	RACHEL
ADRIEL	HANNAH	RAHAB
ANNA	JEZEBEL	REBEKAH
ASENATH	KETURAH	RHODA
ATHALIA	LEAH	RUTH
BATHSHEBA	MARTHA	SALOME
BILHAH	MARY	SAPPHIRA
CANDACE	MARY MAGDALENE	SARAH
DEBORAH	MERAB	TABITHA
DELILAH	MIRIAM	TAMAR
DINAH	NAOMI	VASHTI
ELISABETH	ORPAH	ZILPAH
ESTHER	PHOEBE	ZIPPORAH

13

Famous Couples

```
M A D A L L I C S I R P E R
D D E L I L A H O B S S L U
A L I U Q A B R A H A M I T
V O R A C H E L A I I H S H
I J S A P P H I R A N O A N
D A R E M I S A A C A S B O
B C S A R A H L E M N E E S
G O M E R C T C V O A A T M
J B A C A H A K E B E R H A
E B E Z L E B E Z E J A Y S
```

Draw a line to match the names of the couples.

ABRAHAM	BATHSHEBA
ADAM	DELILAH
AHAB	ELISABETH
ANANIAS	EVE
AQUILA	GOMER
BOAZ	JEZEBEL
DAVID	MARY
HOSEA	PRISCILLA
ISAAC	RACHEL
JACOB	REBEKAH
JOSEPH	RUTH
SAMSON	SAPPHIRA
ZACHARIAS	SARAH

14
The Wanderings of Israel

```
M O S E S V C L C O M M A N D M E N T S V S
A A R D I F M C E N S E R S T E S H C O L R R
N A E A L C B S S E N R E D L I W W H K K E
N R B B V H C O R I A N D E R H O A R A H P
A O M D E A I S R A E L I A N I S T M L R P
I N U E R R T V L S A C R I F I C E A D A O
L E N L T I P R I E S T S F J M O R M S V H
I A A L R O F L R B E J R S B G J P S Z E S
A Y A I U T E G Y P T K A N O C L O U D L S
U B N U M U R M U R C O S O D G V I B T C A
Q A A M P E G F H J M R O I Q E S S L U A R
F L C N E Y F L I E S A R N R L E P O X N G
O T M I T R E A K A U H S O J V S M O N R I
R A Z B S J L E X O D U S W S Q A P D A E A
T R C I S D T R E T A N A R G E M O P E B N
Y H F G A R L I C K U X C A L E B E O Z A T
F A O L M A I R I M P L A G U E S C J O T S
G R E N A F M E L O N S W D R A Z A E L E B
F I R E H C U C U M B E R S I L E P H O D Y
```

AARON	EGYPT	ISRAEL	PASSOVER
ALTAR	ELEAZAR	JOSHUA	PHARAOH
BDELLIUM	EPHOD	KORAH	PLAGUES
BLOOD	ESHCOL	LEEKS	POMEGRANATE
CALEB	EXODUS	MANNA	PRIEST
CALF	FIRE	MELONS	QUAIL
CANAAN	FLIES	MIRIAM	SACRIFICE
CENSERS	FORTY	MITRE	SILVER TRUMPET
CHARIOT	FROGS	MOSES	TABERNACLE
CLOUD	GARLICK	MT. SINAI	WATER
COMMANDMENTS	GIANTS	MURMUR	WILDERNESS
CORIANDER	GRAPES	NUMBERS	
CUCUMBER	GRASSHOPPERS	ONIONS	

15

Sacrifices and Offerings

```
L M R E H E A V E Y R S O F T
E A E C A E P E S F E H T I T
M V N A V G E U F R U O U R L
S T A O L P O N O E G I P S A
S N L W S L N A S E G I F T S
A R E N A R K N T W E E R F A
P U P E S N E C N I K N A R F
S B J N I C U P F L O U R U L
E U B R N S B U L L O C K I A
R S D I E V O D E L T R U T M
T T H A N K S G I V I N G S B
```

BULLOCK

BURNT

DRINK

FIRST FRUITS

FLOUR

FRANKINCENSE

FREE WILL

GIFTS

GOAT

HEAVE

INCENSE

JEALOUSY

LAMB

MEAL

OIL

PEACE

PERSONAL

PIGEON

RAM

SALT

SIN

THANKSGIVING

TITHE

TRESPASS

TURTLEDOVE

WAVE

16
The Mountains of Palestine

```
H Z I R P E N S S N O W B L
E A N A B I E Q N O M R E H
R E L A N V B R X I C H M S
O L L I I I O M C Z T O A O
M M V L H B S I G E R R M N
F I O O A C L A B I I E A O
A Z Y T A R A R A E A B L N
Q I A R H N O H S Y B T E A
U R M B M A B P H V A S K B
N E Z E G I L E A D R H E E
L G X R A Z I M N E I M B L
R O H S H A G S I P M R A L
```

ABARIM	GILBOA	MORIAH
AMALEK	GILEAD	NEBO
ARARAT	HACHILAH	OLIVES
BASHAN	HERMON	PISGAH
BETHEL	HOR	SEIR
CARMEL	HOREB	SINAI
EBAL	LEBANON	TABOR
EPHRAIM	MIZAR	ZION
GERIZIM	MOREH	

17
Palestinian Valleys

```
J Z G B Z S H J S A G I B E O N
E E A I I E B E R A C H A H L O
R C Z D B R B H S L D H C B A H
A E D R Z A R O H Z E K O G M C
K I O K E R O S I I M B O R I I
M I A H P E R H T M N G A O H R
E G D E H G L A T H N N C N C E
G N O L A J A P I O E O O A O J
I E N I T A S H M E C V R M B N
D J I P H T H A H E L C A B O N
D D E R A Z H T L A S A U H E I
O B A C H A R A S H I M H S S H
E B U S K A B C M D L O C H S E
```

ACHOR	HAMON-GOG	REPHAIM
AJALON	HEBRON	SALT
BACA	HINNOM	SHAVEH
BERACHAH	JEHOSHAPHAT	SHITTIM
BOCHIM	JERICHO	SIDDIM
CHARASHIM	JEZREEL	SOREK
ELAH	JIPHTHAHEL	SUCCOTH
ESHCOL	KEZIZ	ZARED
GERAR	LEBANON	ZEBOIM
GIBEON	MEGIDDO	ZEPHATHAH

The Judges of Israel

```
M A S D S O N A J I R O
M A U Q F A O L T A E J
Y H B R T S D O G R I N
E L L I A H B M I B O R
L N U B C A A N D J T B
O N D Z R H T R E Z H R
N O E A S T R T O C N Z
M S K N B H O R N B I J
M M K M D P S L Y S E I
O A T O L E U M A S L D
S S R I I J Z D U E D H
```

ELON
ELI
GIDEON
IBZAN
JAIR
JEPHTHAH
OTHNIEL
SAMSON
SAMUEL
SHAMGAR
TOLA

ABDON   DEBORAH
BARAK   EHUD

19

Kings of Israel

```
J P E K A H T B I N I J
A E I O S A I R M O E E
M I H I M I Z E Z R J H
Z U A O M Z H E O O O A
I B L I A A C B M R R H
M A E L N H O S H E A S
R D B E A A A B J K M A
I A M R M H M Z O E J A
P N I I N T S P U R H B
E A J E H O A S H A E U
H A I H A K E P B M E J
```

JEHOASH
JEHU
JEROBOAM I
JEROBOAM II
JORAM
MENAHEM
NADAB
OMRI
PEKAH
PEKAHIAH
SHALLUM
ZECHARIAH
ZIMRI

AHAB   BAASHA   HOSHEA
AHAZIAH   ELAH   JEHOAHAZ

20
Kings of Judah

```
T M N S A S J E H O R A M H
Z A I J M U Z E A S A Z A A
O N H H A I L A H T A I M I
M A C U Z Z I A H H Z O Z S
M S A B I J A M A A N A J O
A S I T A H P A H S O H E J
H E O I H O M A O B O H E R
T H H A I K E D E Z H J E F
O R E M N M I K A I O H E J
J E J U H E Z E K I A H R O
```

ABIJAM	HEZEKIAH	JOSIAH
AHAZ	JEHOAHAZ	JOTHAM
AHAZIAH	JEHOIACHIN	MANASSEH
AMAZIAH	JEHOIAKIM	REHOBOAM
AMON	JEHORAM	UZZIAH
ASA	JEHOSHAPHAT	ZEDEKIAH
ATHALIAH	JOASH	

21

Kings and Their Domains

```
C A A N O N O S O N E B B U C S
R A S E A C S U T S U G U A E A
E L I A S U R R E J D M Y N O L
A B N S I A K Y B A J O N P H M
H A A R R E R C S P H A R R T E
C R A Z Z E N D A H C U B E N L
U D A I A R P M L H N B A I H A
B B C E R I P M E N A M O R N S
P H A R A O H R M D A R I S U U
A M E L C H I Z E D E K M Y S R
R L A B A B Y L O N U S R Y C E
S A A Y I K A I R Y S S A S Y J
```

Match the names of the kings with their proper dominions.

ASSYRIA	AUGUSTUS CAESAR
BABYLON	BALAK
CANAAN	CYRUS
EGYPT	DARIUS
JERUSALEM	HEROD
MEDES	JABIN
MOAB	MELCHIZEDEK
PERSIA	NEBUCHADNEZZAR
ROMAN EMPIRE	PHARAOH
SALEM	SENNACHERIB

22

Israel's Enemies

```
S N A I R Y S S E P A M O R I T E S
E A S T I N A O M H O I T E S S N Y
T I N R S N S E T I Z Z I R E P O R
I M A O N I T E S L K G I T T E M A
S O I M A A C H T I E A I D I D M N
R S N A I N O D I S A N N O N O A S
E A O A S E T I H T A H C A A M A N
G G L N R E B U S I T E S B A I M A
E I Y S E H R H D N T H I L N T M I
R B B P P I I I A E I T E O A E O N
O B A L T K M V Y S E K I Y C S N O
M L B E I I S B I S I V B T I D I D
A E S A E T A S E T I S U B E J T I
N S K N T B E N E J E B U S A S E Z
S S N A I R Y S S A M S I T E B S S
```

AMALEKITES

AMMONITES

AMORITES

ANAKIMS

ASSYRIANS

BABYLONIANS

CANAANITES

EDOMITES

EGYPTIANS

GESHURITES

GIBLITES

HITTITES

HIVITES

JEBUSITES

MAACHATHITES

MAONITES

MIDIANITES

MOABITES

PERIZZITES

PERSIANS

PHILISTINES

ROMANS

SYRIANS

ZIDONIANS

People from Proverbs

```
B O Y B L E S L U G G A R D W P R O O D
M A D R L A N D N A B S U H W I D E E N
R U C P G N P A J U N E N S H I C S N M
E O M K C N L U U G R A C I O U S K M A
S I S I B O A G S P M O U U L E E E E I
S E D S M I N H T O R W S G L O W L Y D
M A I D E N T T W N D I L B H M O E L E
L R L R R R N E E R F F G M O T H E R S
U I I W C O G R R N A E E H N H Y N U S
F C G P H N S S D G T N N E T F O O O L
H C E U A O O S N R H I D G F T T W L V
T H N R N I R R E A E U O N T O L R A H
I E T L T U J E I C R E L U R U O I W E
A S J U S T E L R P S T L O S O N L Y R
F A S R E D L E F L U G L Y D O O G S O
```

ANGRY	HARLOT	SIMPLE
BACKBITER	HUSBAND	SLUGGARD
BLESSED	JUST	STRANGE WOMAN
CONTENTIOUS	LOWLY	TRANSGRESSOR
DAUGHTERS	MAD	UNJUST
DILIGENT	MAIDEN	UPRIGHT
ELDERS	MERCHANTS	VAIN
FAITHFUL	MOTHERS	WICKED
FATHERS	NAUGHTY	WIFE
FOOLS	ODIOUS	WISE
FRIEND	PRUDENT	WHORE
GLUTTON	RICH	YOUNG
GOOD	RULER	
GRACIOUS	SCORNERS	

24

God Is . . .

```
E  R  I  F  G  N  I  M  U  S  N  O  C  A
U  G  T  S  U  J  T  R  U  E  H  O  L  Y
N  U  N  R  U  H  G  O  O  P  M  S  U  F
C  C  T  I  G  O  I  O  E  U  O  U  F  A
O  O  O  I  R  R  I  R  O  S  S  O  I  I
R  M  R  M  O  E  F  C  U  D  T  E  C  T
R  P  N  L  T  E  F  O  A  L  H  T  R  H
U  A  G  I  C  N  L  F  U  R  I  H  E  F
P  S  L  T  S  A  E  B  U  R  G  G  M  U
T  S  T  O  E  C  W  T  I  S  H  I  H  L
I  I  A  J  V  N  I  P  O  S  G  R  H  T
B  O  E  T  N  E  S  E  R  P  I  N  M  O
L  N  R  G  R  A  E  T  N  G  I  V  O  L
E  A  G  R  E  R  I  G  H  T  U  N  N  L
E  T  E  R  N  A  L  A  T  R  O  M  M  I
B  E  L  B  A  H  C  R  A  E  S  N  U  O
```

A CONSUMING FIRE	IMMORTAL	OMNIPRESENT
A SPIRIT	INVISIBLE	OMNISCIENT
COMPASSIONATE	JEALOUS	PERFECT
ETERNAL	JUST	RIGHT
FAITHFUL	LIGHT	RIGHTEOUS
GLORIOUS	LONGSUFFERING	TRUE
GOOD	LOVE	UNCORRUPTIBLE
GRACIOUS	MERCIFUL	UNSEARCHABLE
GREAT	MOST HIGH	UPRIGHT
HOLY	OMNIPOTENT	WISE

Names and Titles of the Devil

```
G I W I C K E D O N E N O D U B U B E L A I R P
O S L I V E D E H T F O E C N I R P R I I N C R
D I A T I R I P S G N I Y L C E S R A V S A E I
O P L S U S D L I V E E V I L S P I R I T R R N
F T I P S S E L M O T T O B E H T F O L E G N A
T E V I R A V I G O N O E E A W S R E D E R N T
H N E R N D I N L E N L D L N H T E R N N U E E
I O A A O V L B P F I O U I S I M U R D E M N M
S D C T G E E R U A O C G L P T M P E P P M M P
W D C A A R E S L B I R N A I E P M E T E E Y T
O A C C U S E R O F T H E B R E T H R E N N I E
R B U C D A B S E D R U M H I D E R U M T E T R
L A S L E R P R I N C E O F T H I S W O R L D P
D P O L L Y B U B E Z L E E B A P P O L L Y O N
R I A E H T F O R E W O P E H T F O E C N I R P
```

ABADDON

ACCUSER OF THE BRETHREN

ADVERSARY

ANGEL OF THE BOTTOMLESS PIT

APOLLYON

BEELZEBUB

BELIAL

DEVIL

DRAGON

ENEMY

EVIL SPIRIT

FATHER OF LIES

GOD OF THIS WORLD

LIAR

LUCIFER

LYING SPIRIT

MURDERER

OLD SERPENT

PRINCE OF THE DEVILS

PRINCE OF THE POWER OF THE AIR

PRINCE OF THIS WORLD

SATAN

SERPENT

TEMPTER

UNCLEAN SPIRIT

WICKED ONE

26

Prophets and Prophetesses

```
M H A N O J Z J H Z M J A N N A
H A I A S I E A A K O E A G A D
A B L H R D P C I O S H R O A H
G A P A U L H O A D E U M V A U
G K R T C A A B M A S D I I H L
A K H N R H N A E Z C D R H S D
I U A I D I I D H O A A I H I A
N K A O J O A I S A Z H A N L H
A S H A J I H A I A C I M A E E
N P A H P E A H V O R I E H A M
A Z E A J B R A N A C I M T H U
H G M T O E O E H R N O R A A H
O O A A E D B C M N H O J N O A
S M S B L R E L E I K E Z E N N
E L I E U Z D D A D A N I E L H
L E U M A S E L I J A H I D D O
```

AARON	EZEKIEL	JEREMIAH	OBADIAH
AGABUS	GAD	JOEL	ODED
AHIJAH	HABAKKUK	JOHN	PAUL
AMOS	HAGGAI	JONAH	PETER
ANNA	HANANI	MALACHI	SAMUEL
AZARIAH	HOSEA	MICAH	SHEMAIAH
DANIEL	HULDAH	MICAIAH	ZACHARIAS
DAVID	IDDO	MIRIAM	ZADOK
DEBORAH	ISAIAH	MOSES	ZECHARIAH
ELIJAH	JACOB	NAHUM	ZEPHANIAH
ELISHA	JEDUTHUN	NATHAN	
ENOCH	JEHU	NOAH	

27
Marks of Famous Men

Match each man with a characteristic or event

ABRAHAM	BELOVED PHYSICIAN
ADAM	BETRAYER
CAIN	DENIER
DANIEL	DESERTER
DAVID	DOUBTER
JEPHTHAH	FAITHFUL
JEREMIAH	FIRST MAN
JOB	FIRST MURDERER
JOHN MARK	LION'S DEN
JUDAS	MARTYR
LUKE	MEEK
METHUSELAH	MISSIONARY
MOSES	OLDEST MAN
NOAH	PATIENT
PAUL	PSALMIST
PETER	RASH VOW
SAMSON	STRONG
SOLOMON	THE ARK
STEPHEN	WEEPING PROPHET
THOMAS	WISE

```
K F N A M T S E D L O L U R K R A M
E R I R P A T I E N T U H S E W D S
E I A R N A M T S R I F R T E T A M
E T C M S H A L E S U H T E M M E L
M S C K N T O U R L E T P P O E U P
Y I I O R H M E T H U I E H J K S S
R M A W S A O U E W N A T E E M T E
A L N O R D E J R G O F P N R B R S
N A I C I S Y H P D E V O L E B O O
O S B V F R N R T O E J H T M A N M
I P A R Y O O T R U O R R S I N G O
S D E T A P S E A B R A E S A D U J
S N R H H H M D R T Y R E R H R A O
I A L E I N A D J E P H T H A H A H
M L T L O M S M R R R E I N E D E R
L I O N S D E N O M O N O M O L O S
```

28

Bible Doctrines

```
Y G Y G O L O T S I R H C A Y Y
E C C L E S I O L O G Y N S G T
Y O S E M I T T S A L T I O O S
G T I R I P S Y L O H N L Y L I
O L Y G O L O I T R A M A H O R
L S A L V A T I O N O E C Y I H
O S L E G N A P H C R U H C R C
I O Y G O L O T A M U E N P E S
L A N G E L O L O G Y A A O T U
B N O G O G O D C E L B I B O S
I Y A G O H T H E O L O G Y S E
B D Y M E S C H A T O L O G Y J
```

Match each doctrine with the thing or person to which it refers.

ANGELOLOGY	ANGELS
ANTHROPOLOGY	BIBLE
BIBLIOLOGY	CHURCH
CHRISTOLOGY	GOD
ECCLESIOLOGY	HOLY SPIRIT
ESCHATOLOGY	JESUS CHRIST
HAMARTIOLOGY	LAST TIMES
PNEUMATOLOGY	MAN
SOTERIOLOGY	SALVATION
THEOLOGY	SIN

29

Bible Authors

```
N O N Z E P H A N I A H A N O J P
O J E R E M I A H R H C E M O H A
M K H T O D H O B A D I A H E A U
O A E L A U M O S A S R N O Z I I
L R M N M E S O M A K L U K E R H
O Z I A G G A H I I D K K L K A C
S E A H O S E A I H C I U U I H A
L Z H N W E H T T A M A V K E C L
J O E L O M O S E S P O H A L E A
S E M A J E D U J O S H U A D Z M
```

AMOS	JEREMIAH	MICAH
DANIEL	JOEL	MOSES
DAVID	JOHN	NAHUM
EZEKIEL	JONAH	NEHEMIAH
EZRA	JOSHUA	OBADIAH
HABAKKUK	JUDE	PAUL
HAGGAI	LUKE	PETER
HOSEA	MALACHI	SOLOMON
ISAIAH	MARK	ZECHARIAH
JAMES	MATTHEW	ZEPHANIAH

30
Famous Duets

Match each of the following pairs.

ABRAHAM	AARON
ANNA	ABEL
BARNABAS	BARAK
CAIN	CALEB
DAVID	ELISHA
DEBORAH	ESAU
ELIJAH	GOLIATH
EPHRAIM	JAMBRES
HOPHNI	JEROBOAM
HYMENAEUS	JOHN
JACOB	JOHN MARK
JAMES	LOT
JANNES	MANASSEH
JOSHUA	ONESIMUS
LAZARUS	PHILETUS
MOSES	PHINEHAS
PAUL	RICH MAN
PHARES	SILAS
PHILEMON	SIMEON
REHOBOAM	ZARAH

```
S  C  O  J  A  M  B  R  E  S  K  A  R  A  B  T
E  E  C  L  J  S  K  K  D  J  O  G  O  P  A  O
B  L  E  A  I  H  R  M  H  A  J  O  P  A  U  L
M  S  I  M  I  A  A  Y  O  M  V  L  H  A  H  P
A  A  E  J  M  N  M  O  N  E  S  I  M  U  S  H
J  O  H  N  A  E  B  A  C  S  T  A  D  L  O  I
N  L  H  S  N  H  H  B  O  L  O  T  L  A  J  L
S  O  S  A  B  A  N  R  A  B  A  H  S  I  L  E
J  E  E  A  R  A  J  A  O  L  O  Z  A  U  S  T
H  U  R  O  N  A  M  H  C  I  R  R  A  R  S  U
S  B  B  A  C  N  E  A  O  M  U  M  E  R  A  S
P  E  E  O  H  R  A  M  K  P  B  A  O  J  U  Z
D  E  B  L  A  P  H  I  N  E  H  A  S  S  L  S
E  P  H  R  A  I  M  A  A  R  O  N  D  E  E  W
L  E  B  A  A  C  K  N  O  M  E  L  I  H  P  S
```

31

More People from Proverbs

```
A R T F U L U F T I E C E D Y E N E M Y
R O O D R U N K A R D D E T C I L F F A
R E Y O R T S E D L M E S S E N G E R W
E T E R P A V E F U S R S T R A N G E R
B A C K S L I D E R I E T I R C O P Y H
R L N L U F R I S H O D W E N R W D M R
I E I I O U T R T L U W R I F N E A E T
G B S V R N U D R M O U A S T E E R N C
H A A V E G O B B E P T T R R N A R H E
T R I O T O U S E R T N H G D E E I S F
E I N L L D S O L C A N F F B P L S O R
O A T B U L O L K I N G U E U D R W S E
U F S I D Y E D S F A I L H R L L O S P
S U N F A I T H F U L A R E N E M O U S
E S R E V R E P E L T S N P R I N T E D
```

ADULTEROUS	FROWARD	RIGHTEOUS
AFFLICTED	GREEDY	RIOTOUS
BACKSLIDER	HUNTER	SAINTS
BLOODTHIRSTY	HYPOCRITE	SINNERS
CHILDREN	KING	SLOTHFUL
DECEITFUL	MERCIFUL	SON
DESTROYER	MESSENGER	STRANGER
DRUNKARD	OLD	TALEBEARER
DUMB	PERFECT	UNFAITHFUL
ENEMY	PERVERSE	UNGODLY
EVIL	POOR	VIRTUOUS
FAIR	PRINCE	WRATHFUL
FALSE WITNESS	PROUD	
FOWLER	PURE	

32

The Books of the New Testament

```
S N A I U R K R A M O C T T N I A I
P R T Y M S I I T I M O T H Y C O G
M S D H S N J E O G A L A L T O C S
E E S T T A O H P N N O B S U R A W
A F S N A I N O L A S S E H T I I E
S E W W M H S N E D C S U S N N P R
R N E P M T T N F O I I N D J T P B
K H A Q H N H O J S N A I S E H P E
T O M I I I E W R S M N O X M I H H
W J S R N R L K A O E S M B U A I L
E I I N O O E I R X T R U Q J N L L
H I T H A C L V P T P R B S J S E I
T I I O S I N A E P C E E U U I M J
T A M J A I T Y S L I M R T D I O O
A S O I E K T A B S A A I E E I N H
M C T I K M A O L J E T N Z T P Z N
R A H U U L A S U A I H I S H O I P
A T Y Y L C D D Q U G O T O H I O J
K U O R E T E P I I V U J I N C A T
```

MATTHEW	EPHESIANS	HEBREWS
MARK	PHILIPPIANS	JAMES
LUKE	COLOSSIANS	I PETER
JOHN	I THESSALONIANS	II PETER
ACTS	II THESSALONIANS	I JOHN
ROMANS	I TIMOTHY	II JOHN
I CORINTHIANS	II TIMOTHY	III JOHN
II CORINTHIANS	TITUS	JUDE
GALATIANS	PHILEMON	REVELATION

33
Biblical Occupations

Draw a line to the biblical occupation of each person listed below.

ARMY CAPTAIN	AARON
CARPENTER	ALEXANDER
CENTURION	AMOS
COPPERSMITH	AQUILA
CUP BEARER	CORNELIUS
EVANGELIST	DANIEL
FISHERMAN	DAVID
HERDSMAN	ESTHER
HUNTER	EZRA
KING	JOSEPH
MISSIONARY	LUKE
PHYSICIAN	LYDIA
PRIEST	MALCHUS
PROPHET	MATTHEW
QUEEN	NAAMAN
SCRIBE	NEHEMIAH
SELLER OF PURPLE	NIMROD
SERVANT	ONESIMUS
SHEPHERD	PAUL
SLAVE	PETER
TAX COLLECTOR	PHILIP
TENTMAKER	SOLOMON

```
Q N E H E M A L C H U S T S U L D T C Y
U A O A M O S Y O S L A V E U O S E U R
E M D I P R E D N A X E L A R R E H P A
E R R M R S U I C C A P P M V D R P B N
N E E I U Q A O P R A I N A D V O E O
R H H H E I T L P U M N L V D M A R A I S
E S P E S L L N P H Y S I C I A N P R S
K I E N T E V F E S C D H A V T T R E S
A F H E C N O D R C A R P E N T E R R I
M E S T O R J O S E P H L U A H G I E M
T Z O R E O A R M S T H U N T E R N B A
N R A L A C L E I N A D K S E W A K I N
E A L I U Q A U T S I L E G N A V E R K
T E N A A M A N H A N A M S D R E H C S
S R E T E P S U M I S E N O M O L O S O
```

Themes of New Testament Books

```
T I H C P C H R I S T I A N E X P E R I E N C E F A
W A Y O T A L O V E E X E M P L I F I E D E F I E D
A H R N H C U E C N E N I M E E R P S T S I R H C M
L O O T O S U L T N E M D N A M M O C S T S I R H C
E L L E L I A D S S Y T I E D S I H N I T S I R H C
C D G N I V I L N A I T S I R H C L A C I T C A R P
A I D D N S T H O O U R D O G F O L E P S O G S G O
R N N I G C Y Y C O C T H C Y D U N T N E C A R C W
G G A N L N E A E H C N H C R I T R H C H L A H A P
Y T G G O I I D D I R R A O F U R T U R V C U L R F
B H N F V I D K I T I I L I R O R D I A C R K I E E
N E I O M R T F E S S E S Y T I D S R E C I E L U L
O T R R E E E A T H H A M I F S T O B H N T L V S L
I R E T S P E T M T T I L S A S I Y O G S O O N S O
T U F H S X H H F M S T S L R N D R I H S L H I N W
A T F E I E T O Y S U N S E K A D N H H T I R C O S
V H U F M X Y T I S N S T I A E T N I C U S I H C H
L E S A O A E O N O R U N Y R R H C R U H C E H T I
A K N I D I N O C T R E R O U H S U F F E R I N P
S N O T D S C M E N N O I T C R C H R I S I A N R C
R I E H T N A V R E S E H T T S I R H C A L T A R P
```

CHRISTIAN CONDUCT	FELLOWSHIP
CHRISTIAN EXPERIENCE	FIRST CENTURY MISSIONS
CHRIST IN HIS DEITY	GOSPEL OF GOD
CHRIST'S COMMANDMENT	HOLDING THE TRUTH
CHRIST'S PREEMINENCE	LAST DAYS
CHRIST'S RETURN	LOVE EXEMPLIFIED
CHRIST THE KING	PAUL'S AUTHORITY
CHRIST THE MAN	PRACTICAL CHRISTIAN LIVING
CHRIST THE SERVANT	PRIESTHOOD OF CHRIST
CHURCH ORDER	SALVATION BY GRACE
CONSUMMATION	SUFFERING AND GLORY
CONTENDING FOR THE FAITH	THE CHURCH
DAY OF THE LORD	WALKING IN TRUTH

35
The Christmas Story

```
C S D S W E J E H T F O G N I K
A D T R G M Y R R H R E G N A M
E R H D O E S M A E R D E E M B
S E H T O L C G N I L D D A W S
A H W A D R E A A N I U R R S B
R P I X T T E H E N J Y H I D E
A E S I I D A H T P G O M Y L T
U H E N D I V A D F O E S U O H
G S M G I J E S U S O O L E G L
U L E U N A M M E N F Y C S P E
S H N E G Y P T R N I G R I V H
T F I R S T B O R N S O N O I E
U S A A N N A L E I R B A G L M
S T T E S N E C N I K N A R F G
S G O O D W I L L R U O I V A S
```

After all the words in the list are found in the puzzle, the unused letters will spell out an appropriate phrase.

ANGELS	GOLD	MYRRH
ANNA	GOOD TIDINGS	PEACE
BETHLEHEM	GOOD WILL	SAVIOUR
CAESAR AUGUSTUS	HEROD	SHEPHERDS
DREAMS	HOUSE OF DAVID	SIMEON
EGYPT	JESUS	STAR
EMMANUEL	JOSEPH	SWADDLING CLOTHES
FIRSTBORN SON	JUDEA	TAXING
FRANKINCENSE	KING OF THE JEWS	THE INN
GABRIEL	MANGER	VIRGIN
GLORY OF THE LORD	MARY	WISE MEN

36

Genealogy of Jesus, (Matthew 1)

```
E B A D A N I M A S A A A B I U D D
S T S I R H C S U S E J C J O I J U
R M B A J R A Z A E L E O H V O N I
O A A U I J O D S J O S I A A O Z L
M H D T A K O B E A I S D T M Z O E
E A P C T C E C O A L E H O I I R D
S R O E A H H Z S A B A L I H A O O
J B O A S O A M E O M O T A C S B B
O A S Z N O O N J O S A P H A T A O
R I R I A O J E S E L I A K I M B C
A N A A S S O N S E R A H P O E E A
M S A L M O N O S E S S A N A M L J
```

ABIA	ELIUD	JUDAS
ABIUD	ESROM	MANASSES
ABRAHAM	EZEKIAS	MATTHAN
ACHAZ	ISAAC	NAASSON
ACHIM	JACOB	OBED
AMINADAB	JACOB	OZIAS
AMON	JECHONIAS	PHARES
ARAM	JESSE	ROBOAM
ASA	JESUS CHRIST	SADOC
AZOR	JOATHAM	SALATHIEL
BOOZ	JORAM	SALMON
DAVID	JOSAPHAT	SOLOMON
ELEAZAR	JOSEPH	ZOROBABEL
ELIAKIM	JOSIAS	

37
Genealogy of Jesus (Luke 3)

```
J Z O R O B A B E L J O A N N A A S S O N
O L E E L E L A M T O A D U J A C O B S A
S N E R E N O M L A S O R O N M A R A I N
E P N O V I C H M H E S S E E G G A N M O
P H O H I O M E U T P E R L D I L S E E J
H A C C S S A L A T H I E L I E Z E R O E
E L H A M A M I N A D A B R A H A M V N S
B E M N A H T A A M S E R A H P C D A I U
E C A A T S M K T A H T T A M A E L U J S
R A S N T D I I H T Z O O B G E S S E J E
E I E N A T H M A D A V I D E A L E H M L
D N H A T N A P N N H T E S A R U C H I M
E A R J H A I T E N O S H J O S E P H E O
B N L M I D D A H S G O D I E M E S S I D
O E O A A D U J C A O M A D A X A H P R A
J M R E S R O M I R O J A L A S U H T A M
```

ABRAHAM	ENOS	JOSE	MATTATHIAS	PHARES
ADAM	ER	JOSEPH	MATTHAT	RAGAU
ADDI	ESLI	JOSEPH	MATTHAT	RHESA
AMINADAB	ESROM	JOSEPH	MELCHI	SALA
AMOS	GOD	JOSEPH	MELCHI	SALATHIEL
ARAM	HEBER	JUDA	MELEA	SALMON
ARPHAXAD	HELI	JUDA	MENAN	SARUCH
BOOZ	ISAAC	JUDA	NAASSON	SEM
CAINAN	JACOB	LAMECH	NACHOR	SEMEI
CAINAN	JANNA	LEVI	NAGGE	SETH
COSAM	JARED	LEVI	NATHAN	SIMEON
DAVID	JESSE	MAATH	NAUM	THARA
ELIAKIM	JESUS	MALELEEL	NERI	ZOROBABEL
ELIEZER	JOANNA	MATHUSALA	NOE	
ELMODAM	JONAN	MATTATHA	OBED	
ENOCH	JORIM	MATTATHIAS	PHALEC	

The Parables of Christ

```
N T R E E R T G I F N E R R A B E W E
L A E P E A R L T H E N N A M R B E U
R I C H F O L A N I E A V A I U S E N
E B U I D I L E W O T Z R A I E E R J
W R D O L E N I V I R R I L N G T U U
O E E I N B R O R P I R D A G R P S S
S V S T M E U A M A R I R G L E R A T
T L S P E U M P G M N C A E E A O E S
E I N W O A S E D G O M A H A T D R T
N S O E S U F T T N T V S E V S I T E
V T S D T E N O A A A T S W E U G N W
I S O A A A W D R R S E E O N P A E A
R O W S Z E R E S O D A E O N P L D R
G L T P R I S S L D E S M S N E S D D
I U S A V T E N W A R D E S I R O I T
N S R E R O B A L O M U L E V R N H E
S L N L O O F H C I R H O U D R A W N
I I M P O R T U N A T E W I D O W H O
G T N A V R E S L U F I C R E M N U P
```

BARREN FIG TREE	PEARL
BUILDING TOWER	PHARISEE AND PUBLICAN
DRAW NET	POUNDS
GOOD SAMARITAN	PRODIGAL SON
GREAT SUPPER	RICH FOOL
HIDDEN TREASURE	SOWER
IMPORTUNATE WIDOW	TALENTS
LABORERS	TARES
LEAVEN	TEN VIRGINS
LOST SHEEP	TWO SONS
LOST SILVER	UNJUST STEWARD
MARRIAGE FEAST	UNMERCIFUL SERVANT
MUSTARD SEED	

39

Two-Word Titles

```
L  P  S  E  A  R  A  C  B  J  S  R  P  O
S  E  A  L  S  M  A  A  U  S  E  S  O  J
U  L  B  U  P  A  R  S  C  T  S  C  N  N
T  Y  A  B  L  N  T  Y  E  H  L  U  T  G
S  S  S  A  A  U  P  P  M  A  R  K  I  H
U  I  R  B  S  E  S  I  U  D  C  I  U  O
G  A  A  R  A  P  U  D  L  D  M  U  S  S
U  S  B  N  O  M  I  S  C  A  R  I  O  T
A  T  S  O  O  U  G  P  R  E  T  E  R  J
J  U  D  A  S  M  R  Y  I  U  O  E  O  O
M  A  G  D  A  L  E  N  E  S  L  H  P  S
Y  L  O  H  S  U  S  E  J  O  N  H  N  E
```

Connect each of the first names with the correct surname.

BARSABAS	AUGUSTUS
CAESAR	BARNABAS
CLAUDIUS	CHRIST
HOLY	GHOST
JESUS	ISCARIOT
JOHN	JUSTUS
JOSES	LYSIAS
JUDAS	MAGDALENE
LEBBAEUS	MARK
MARY	PAULUS
PONTIUS	PETER
SERGIUS	PILATE
SIMON	THADDAEUS

40

Words and Their Biblical Definitions

Connect each word with the proper biblical definition.

ASHER	APPOINTED
BABEL	A PRINCE OF GOD
BETHEL	A TROOP
BOANERGES	BITTER
CEPHAS	BOOTHS
CORBAN	CONFUSION
EDOM	DRAWN OUT
EMMANUEL	GIFT
EVE	GOD WITH US
GAD	HAPPY
ISRAEL	HOUSE OF GOD
JESUS	MANY
LEGION	MOTHER OF ALL LIVING
MARAH	RED
MESSIAS	SAVIOUR
MOSES	SENT
SETH	SONS OF THUNDER
SILOAM	STONE
SUCCOTH	TAKEN OUT OF MAN
WOMAN	THE CHRIST

```
H S A H P E C R E D N U H T F O S N O S
T E Y P P A H O U S E O F G O D T F I G
E T S I R H C E H T A P P O I N T E D A
S L A G N I V I L L A F O R E H T O M
P S E G R E N A O B S U H T I W D O G A
O U A B S P E C S H U B S U S E J M M N
O C M V A T A K E N O U T O F M A N A Y
R C A O I B O R N O R C O N F U S I O N
T O R G S O I N T I F E E W O M A N L A
A T A A S E U H E G I G D A R E T T I B
E H H D E I S R A E L C O R B A N H S A
E V E M M A N U E L D O M D L E H T E B
```

41

Who Was Spoken To?

1. John 1:22 _____
2. 1:50 _____
3. 2:4 _____
4. 3:7 _____
5. 4:24 _____
6. 4:50 _____
7. 5:8 _____
8. 6:5 _____
9. 7:20 _____
10. 8:11 _____
11. 9:7 _____
12. 10:25 _____
13. 11:25 _____
14. 11:43 _____
15. 12:7 _____
16. 13:21 _____
17. 17:16 _____
18. 18:36 _____
19. 20:29 _____
20. 21:22 _____

```
S A M A N A M O W E E J U D A
U W A T H A M A T H R A O P H
S L E T P E M A I P I L I H P
E E R J N E L T H A M O S I N
S A M A R I T A N W O M A N E
M N A G P S C E P E T B D P N
N A M O W S U O R E T L U D A
T H R D E T E R D J H O J N J
A T R Y R R A M A E O N P E E
N A M D N I L B E Z M N S M S
M N O B L E M A N D A U H P I
D A D I S C I P L E S L S E S
```

42

The Crucifixion

```
            S D L E I F S R E T T O P S J
            S L D E H S I N I F S I T I E
            O O I G R L A Y A R T E B M W
            R S N O A M R U O H H T X I S
            C I T B E H O L D T H Y S O N
            G C T S P C A I A P H A S N O
D J S A B B A R A B H R U O H H T N I N M O N O M I S R O S H
O E T E G T U F E T I N A H T H C A B A S A M A L I L E I L E
O S N R R O E R E H R S N R O H T F O N W O R C N I K T T I B
L E E I C L R G A T T E A R G C R U C I F Y O Y V I N E G A R
B E A S A D U J R U Y O M M L T E E L O M A S E N I A P S N E
K L E M O L A S T R P E M R O S S Y E A T T I G S U S E J E W
P A R R A D I S H T I R A Y G C R R G D S L O S L A I N E R G
W A T T E R E U Q S E L A O H A K D I O A F S J U D A H S I F
            U I C O R E V T A E H H T Y E
            A T E T D L T L D G R H T L S
            K A S S A A A E O E L E Y N I S
            E H O C I N R H R J O N E T E
            T W F A E D T K E I W H M A N
            A A S S E P A W N A U Y E N T
            L S I T U R S R T E L M V B I
            I P L E E J U E A A S A A C W
            P E V D H S R T T P I S P O E
            U A E E E N O I R U T N E C S
            G R R F A N N A S O F A H K L
            S O L D I E R S W A T E T R A
            D E L E B O R T E L R A C S F
```

ANNAS	CROWN OF THORNS
BARABBAS	CRUCIFY
BEHOLD THY MOTHER	DARKNESS
BEHOLD THY SON	DENIAL
BETRAYAL	EARTHQUAKE
BLOOD	ELI ELI LAMA SABACHTHANI
CAIAPHAS	FALSE WITNESSES
CALVARY	GAVE UP THE GHOST
CENTURION	GETHSEMANE
COAT	GOLGOTHA
COCK	GREEK
CROSS	HEBREW

HEROD
I THIRST
IT IS FINISHED
JESUS
JEWS
JUDAS
KING OF THE JEWS
LATIN
LOTS CASTED
MALEFACTORS
MARY
MARY MAGDALENE
MOCKERY
NAILS
NINTH HOUR
PARADISE
PETER
PILATE
POTTER'S FIELD
PRAETORIUM
SALOME
SCARLET ROBE
SCOURGING
SIMON
SIXTH HOUR
SLAIN
SOLDIERS
SPEAR

THE PAVEMENT
THIRTY PIECES OF SILVER
THREE DAYS
TORTURE
TRIAL
VEIL
VINEGAR
WATER
WHAT IS TRUTH

43

Names and Titles of Christ

```
C O U N S E L O R O T A I D E M M A N U E L L
L E N O Y L O H D R O L E H T F O L E G N A
L E G O V E R N O R O O D I V A D F O N O S
I N T H E A D O F T H E C H U R C H O F E O
G O S D R E H P E H S D O O G P W I S C K N
H T E N O I T C E R R U S E R A T S O I D O
T S I O B R A N C H W D M I Y A E N N D R F
O R R W O R D L E T O O N E V J D G O W E G
F E P D A V D N P G R C N L S A E G F O H O
T N H J I D I O Y H E U A D D S F E M R P D
H R G E E V V T G O A S T A E O I N A D E I
E O I J E H H O F F F A M H D R L A N O H V
W C H H E G O P C O O L N R R L F Q H F S A
O F T N I S E V N A I B O D D E O U O L F D
R E A M O A U I A F T W M V O S D R L I E F
L I E N C R A S E H T E M A I M A E H F I O
D H R E H T A F G N I T S A L R E V E E H T
T C G A P S G N I K F O G N I K R G I M C O
G O R A T S G N I N R O M N A R B R A O E O
D K C O R S W E J E H T F O G N I K N I R R
```

ADVOCATE

ALPHA AND OMEGA

ANGEL OF THE LORD

BRANCH

BREAD OF LIFE

CAPTAIN OF SALVATION

CHIEF CORNERSTONE

CHIEF SHEPHERD

COUNSELOR

DOOR

EMMANUEL

GOD

GOOD SHEPHERD

GOVERNOR

GREAT HIGH PRIEST

HEAD OF THE CHURCH

HOLY ONE

I AM

JEHOVAH

JESUS

KING

KING OF KINGS

KING OF THE JEWS

LAMB OF GOD

LIGHT OF THE WORLD

LIFE

LORD

MEDIATOR

MESSIAH

MORNING STAR

PRINCE OF PEACE

REDEEMER

RESURRECTION

ROCK

ROOT OF DAVID

SAVIOUR

SECOND ADAM

SON OF DAVID

SON OF GOD

SON OF MAN

STAR

THE EVERLASTING FATHER

THE MIGHTY GOD

THE VINE

TRUTH

WAY

WONDERFUL

WORD

WORD OF GOD

WORD OF LIFE

Names and Titles of the Holy Spirit

```
T H E N I G H O L Y G H O S T T T R
R H H W O N K N O W L E D G E H A I
E N E O N I T P H H O T D A E E D T
T R O L L O T T T I R I P S Y L O H
R N N S O I U A H E Y R P P C W P G
O C E T E R N A L S P I R I T I T I
F O H M T H D E P E R P U R R S I M
M U D R G L T I S I V S D I U D O I
O N G N I D N A T S R E D N U O N G
C S M F M S U G R A C E R G I M O H
O E E N F H T J O R P R O P H E C Y
M L R E H T A F E H T F S G O G O D
```

The names without an * indicate "THE SPIRIT OF."

ADOPTION	KNOWLEDGE
CHRIST	LIFE
COMFORTER*	MIGHT
COUNSEL	PROPHECY
ETERNAL SPIRIT*	REVELATION
FREE SPIRIT*	THE FATHER
GLORY	THE LORD
GOD	THE SON
GRACE	THE SPIRIT*
HOLINESS	TRUTH
HOLY GHOST*	UNDERSTANDING
HOLY SPIRIT*	WISDOM
JUDGMENT	

45
Places of Paul's Travels

```
C L E P H E S U S O O S A M O S A S
A H Y H C A U D A I P R U S Y T O I
C R I S Y R I A N A L A H T S T O D
O S A O T G M C T H P O T O E O S O
O H S U S R A T I H X V P A D L S N
S A T Y R E A R O L E S I A R E I G
N V A N C L C O C C I N I W E A S M
C N E F I E I A H A O C S U E N O U
M D R A E R N S M D U I A C G I H P
U I E M O R O E E E F P L Y M L P R
I S B A M E L C L C A P A P U O A H
L P N Q R O A E A Y I I M R I E P E
L H U E T M S E S S T L I U N T S G
Y R D P V S S R U U A I S S O U A I
G Y Z E G A E G R C L H M T C P T U
O G P H R Y H E E S A P Y A I P R M
R I X E B B T R J A G S R Y E A Y A
T A A F Y E E M I M P Y A R E S L R
A I C A R H T O M A S O G B I W A S
S S O C N I D U S D F A L A T G I L
```

ANTIOCH
ASSOS
ATHENS
ATTALIA
BEREA
CAESAREA
CAUDA
CHIOS
CILICIA
CNIDUS
COOS
CORINTH
CRETE
CYPRUS
DAMASCUS
DERBE

EPHESUS
FAIR HAVENS
GALATIA
GREECE
ICONIUM
JERUSALEM
LASEA
LYSTRA
MACEDONIA
MILETUS
MITYLENE
MYRA

MYSIA
NEAPOLIS
PAPHOS
PATARA
PERGA
PHILIPPI
PHRYGIA
PTOLEMAIS
PUTEOLI
RHEGIUM
RHODES
ROME

SALAMIS
SAMOS
SAMOTHRACIA
SELEUCIA
SIDON
SYRACUSE
SYRIA
TARSUS
THESSALONICA
TROAS
TROGYLLIUM
TYRE

46
Who Said It?

Fill in the blanks below with the correct speaker.

LYDIA   MAN OF MACEDONIA   EVIL SPIRIT

KING AGRIPPA   JAILKEEPER   SIMON

SAUL   PAUL   GAMALIEL

PHILIP   TOWN CLERK   THE TWELVE

ANANIAS   GALLIO   STEPHEN

JAMES   FESTUS   ETHIOPIAN EUNUCH

LUKE   AGABUS   CORNELIUS

CHRIST   ANGEL OF GOD

PETER   DEMON-POSSESSED DAMSEL

1. Acts 1:1 _____

2. 1:8 _____

3. 3:19 _____

4. 5:35 _____

5. 6:2 _____

6. 7:59 _____

7. 8:19 _____

8. 8:36 _____

9. 8:37 _____

10. 9:5 _____

11. 9:17 _____

12. 10:33 _____

13. 15:13 _____

14. 16:9 _____

15. 16:15 _____

16. 16:17 _____

17. 16:30 _____

```
P H I A P P I R G A G N I K B U S A M A G
F A D J A I L K E E P E R S E D M A I D L
S E U S E J Y E M A J P V S I H C N U Q U
P A S U B A G A M A I T E L N D O L E L K
A A I T D M G A N L S F L E E D P I L O R
H C U N U E N A I P O I H T E W E T E E O
G G M S A S M H H G L P M C M V T W T N I
M A G U U R P E O A E A A O I E R E E W L
G M M B P I N D N T I M N L N K P E H O L
C S A A L T L A S D F E S I M U N L T T A
C H L S L S N E E O S P I R I L I V E E G
P U R E N I A J N A I H H E R T C S D W Q
S A P I A H E A K R E L C N W O T C C W T
L A U S S C M L I D O G O F L E G N A S E
P A L L U T H T R E L C A D A I D Y L Y A
D E M O N P O S S E S S E D D A M S E L Q
```

18. 17:22 _____

19. 18:14 _____

20. 19:15 _____

21. 19:36 _____

22. 21:11 _____

23. 25:12 _____

24. 26:28 _____

25. 27:24 _____

47

"Tion" Words

```
N S L N O I T U C E S R E P Q P N O I T
O A A A O I T O V E C O R Q U E A R O D
I L M L M I L O C O M O T H E R T D N E
T V E E V E C A N T P I O N S D I I O M
A A N T R A N S F I G U R A T I O N I O
C T T O T R O T T N N E N O I T N A T N
I I I I I L I I A A O O N N O I O T O S
F O O N A T A T D T M I I E N O I I M T
I N N T O T C O I T I B T T R N T O O R
T I I I I T P E T O S O I A A A I N R A
C O N O I T C F F F A E N T T L T O P T
N T N O I T A C I F I R U P I U E I N I
A A N O I T A R O D A E M Q U O P V O O
S N N I N O I T A S N E P S I D N E E N
D E V O T I O N O I T C E R R U S E R R
```

ADOPTION	PERSECUTION
ADORATION	PETITION
AFFECTION	PROMOTION
AMBITION	PROPITIATION
CONSOLATION	PURIFICATION
DEMONSTRATION	QUESTION
DEVOTION	REPUTATION
DISPENSATION	RESURRECTION
GENERATION	REVELATION
LAMENTATION	SALVATION
MENTION	SANCTIFICATION
NATION	TEMPTATION
ORDINATION	TRANSFIGURATION
PERDITION	VOCATION

48
More "Tion" Words

```
P I A B O M I N A T I O N O I T E P X E T
R T N J N O I T C I L F F A N K N N C X N
E E S S U P C O N T E N I O T B O O O C O
G I S U P S N O T I O N I I E E I I N O I
E O P U P I T P N I G T H L R F T T V M T
N N R E P P R I T S A N O N P E A A O M A
E O O Z R E L A F R E V O O R M L C C U R
R I P I N F R I T I A C D I E U U I A N R
A T I A T I E S C I C D R T T L B D T I E
T A T M M R I C T A O A I A A A I E I C V
I S I D K N O Z T I T N T T T R D O A N O
O U A M I R E T W I T I O I I I T E N T C
N C E M U L A T X N O I O T O O O D P I C
X C D E D I C A T E J N O N N N N N O O R
P A R T I T I O N Y F O U N D A T I O N Q
R E D E M P T I O N N O I T A T C E P X E
```

ABOMINATION	FOUNDATION
ACCUSATION	INSPIRATION
ADMINISTRATION	INTERPRETATION
ADMIRATION	JUSTIFICATION
AFFLICTION	OPERATION
CONSECRATION	PARTITION
CONVERSATION	PERFECTION
CONVOCATION	REDEMPTION
DEDICATION	REGENERATION
EMULATION	SUPERSTITION
EXCOMMUNICATION	SUPPLICATION
EXPECTATION	TRADITION
EXTORTION	TRIBULATION

Names of the Saved

```
L I V E L Y S T O N E S R I E H W O L L E F
O S C O L N E S O C H O S E N V E S S E L S
R E H F R I E N D S O F G O D L E N R N D C
D S O T S R G O B E L E V E R S V R E S R H
O S S N V T D H O L Y S P R I T A R D T O I
O E E A E S O E T O P E B M E N R D E F L L
H N N D S I G E H S E C O F R I E N E D E D
T T O I S R F P I H O R Y T L A S L M B H R
S I N S E H O A S E P F N L R S L E E E T E
E W E C L C S F E F L R T C D O N L D S F N
I B S I S F R O O L E V H H W O O H O D O O
R E E P J O I N T H E I R S E V G N F I D F
P R O L S S E M T S L C E E E W S E T C E L
L T H E I R H E E D U R T D S O O A H P S I
A H C S D E R M R N V J O O F C N R E T S G
Y E H L I B V E B A O F E G F Y S S L E E H
O C I O S M N E N E G F O H L G F O O D L T
R H S V C E T T R O M D G O T S O J R O B N
C I T E P M S H D S E T H O G H G D D L V A
O L R B E R N E R H T E R B D E V O L E B I
D O G F O N E R D L I H C H R I S T I A N S
```

BELIEVERS	DISCIPLES
BELOVED BRETHREN	ELECT OF GOD
BELOVED OF GOD	FELLOW HEIRS
BLESSED OF THE LORD	FELLOW SERVANTS
CHILDREN OF GOD	FRIENDS OF GOD
CHILDREN OF LIGHT	HEIRS OF GOD
CHILDREN OF PROMISE	HOLY NATION
CHOSEN ONES	HOLY PEOPLE
CHOSEN VESSELS	JOINT HEIRS
CHRISTIANS	LIGHTS OF THE WORLD
DEAR CHILDREN	LIVELY STONES

MEMBERS OF CHRIST
MEN OF GOD
REDEEMED OF THE LORD
ROYAL PRIESTHOOD
SAINTS
SALT
SERVANTS
SHEEP
SONS OF GOD
THE GODLY
THE JUST
VESSELS
WITNESSES

50
Christian Characteristics

```
N A M S T E A D F A S T Z J U S T H W
S I K Y T R I G H T E O U S P Q H U D
S S E L E M A L B T H C A N L F G M E
U M E O K G U I L E L E S S U E I B L
O X M H O F Y A B N C D R E F A R L I
L D F D I L U F H T I A F E H R P E F
A G L C W T H G N I V O L R C I U I E
E Y R O J K R L M V N O P U T N Q R D
Z E L S B P R U D E N T T P A G I U N
M V W O B E D I E N T X A Y W Z B S U
```

ATTENTIVE	JUST	SINCERE
BLAMELESS	LOVING	STEADFAST
BOLD	LOWLY	TRUE
FAITHFUL	MEEK	UNDEFILED
FEARING	MERCIFUL	UPRIGHT
GODLY	OBEDIENT	WATCHFUL
GUILELESS	PRUDENT	ZEALOUS
HOLY	PURE	
HUMBLE	RIGHTEOUS	

51

The Christian Walk

```
D C I R C U M S P E C T L Y L E H T Y B M
O S D N A M M M O C I U P R I G H T L Y O
G I A S C H I L D R E N O F L I G H T L D
F L N I T H E L I G T H T I I I P S S U S
O H T T N E I P S D O G E R O F E B E C I
Y T I I H I S T O R Y W I S U M D V N R W
H T A F T E R T H E S P I R I T O O O I N
T I F E H I L I H T I A F Y B L H L H C I
R A F T E R H I S C O M M A N D M E N T S
O F N W R O W T G O O D N I I M H I M A I
W I O O R W O R T H Y O F T H E L O R D I
N E W O R T H Y O F T H E V O C A T I O N
H O N E F I L F O S S E N W E N N I N T O
```

1. Ps. 56:13 _ _ _ _ _ _   _ _ _
2. Ps. 84:11 _ _ _ _ _ _ _ _ _
3. Rom. 6:4 _ _   _ _ _ _ _ _ _   _ _   _ _ _ _
4. Rom. 8:1 _ _ _ _   _ _ _   _ _ _ _ _ _ _
5. 2 Cor. 5:7 _ _   _ _ _ _ _
6. Gal. 5:16 _ _   _ _ _   _ _ _ _ _ _
7. Eph. 4:1 _ _ _ _ _ _   _ _   _ _ _   _ _ _ _ _ _ _ _
8. Eph. 5:2 _ _   _ _ _ _
9. Eph. 5:8 _ _   _ _ _ _ _ _ _   _ _   _ _ _ _
10. Eph. 5:15 _ _ _ _ _ _ _ _ _ _ _ _ _
11. Col. 1:10 _ _ _ _ _ _   _ _   _ _ _   _ _ _ _
12. Col. 2:6 _ _   _ _ _
13. Col. 4:5 _ _   _ _ _ _ _ _
14. 1 Thess. 2:12 _ _ _ _ _ _   _ _   _ _ _
15. 1 Thess. 4:12 _ _ _ _ _ _ _ _
16. 1 John 1:7 _ _   _ _ _   _ _ _ _ _
17. 2 John 6 _ _ _ _ _   _ _ _   _ _ _ _ _ _ _ _ _ _ _
18. 3 John 4 _ _   _ _ _ _ _

52

Names of the Wicked

```
W H E L L O R T R A N S G R E S S O R S
I N I M N E R D L I H C D E S R U C E R
S S S R E O D D E K C I W I N E F N B E
T S W I C K E D O N E S O W O P O O E O
T H E D E V I L G E N E R A T I O N L D
E E E N C S V Y L D O A K R T V L E L L
S L V F D I I I L E T S E A E F S R I I
E V I D L E B N O H D A R T N O T D O V
T E N E D E K G N G U E S D E N H L U E
A H V E L I S C T E N R O S M O E I S C
B E E I M I C H I E R G F T I I S H C N
O N A W N Y I I G W F S I N E T C C H E
R L E E I S L L N O I T N E S A O T I I
P E R M W C U D S I U E I P O R R N L D
E S D O L F K R O G Q I Q R F E N E D E
R F R I N I E E U G Q U U E G N F D R B
E L O I R T V N D U N Q I S O E U U E O
D N S O A P L E I O B U T T D G L P N S
U U N H O Y L D O G N U Y L Y L O M R I
N I S F O S T N A V R E S D E K C I W D
```

*—"CHILDREN OF"

BELIAL*

CURSED CHILDREN

DISOBEDIENCE*

ENEMIES OF GOD

EVIL DOERS

EVIL GENERATION

EVIL MEN

FOOLS

GENERATION
  OF VIPERS

HATERS OF GOD

HELL*

IMPUDENT CHILDREN

INIQUITY*

LYING CHILDREN

PRIDE*

REBELLIOUS CHILDREN

REPROBATES

SERPENTS

SERVANTS OF SIN

SINFUL GENERATION

SINNERS

THE DEVIL*

THE FLESH*

THE SCORNFUL

THE WICKED ONE*

THIS WORLD*

TRANSGRESSORS

UNGODLY

UNGODLY MEN

WICKED DOERS

WICKEDNESS*

WICKED ONES

WICKED SERVANTS

WORKERS
  OF INIQUITY

WRATH*

53

Types of Ministers

```
S E R V A N T S O F G O D A D W D
T R S S S R O D A S S A B M A E A
E S E T R T D O O R R A C T A A C
V T L H E E R G A V S E C C R H S
A E T A C W R F W D E H H P O N O
N W S N S A A O O O M R W C O S C
G A O G P R E S B E R I S C A O E
E R P E O A H R N A T K A E D E D
L D A L H S S E P N L E E L E R T
I S E S S R S T E E D L E R S R S
S O L D I E R S O F C H R I S T S
T F D O B L S I M R S R E D L E N
S G O S R E G N E S S E M E N E S
P O R O S I B I S H E P H E R D S
A D S M E N E M F O S R E H S I F
```

AMBASSADORS

ANGELS

APOSTLES

BISHOPS

DEACONS

ELDERS

EVANGELISTS

FISHERS OF MEN

LABORERS

MESSENGERS

MINISTERS OF GOD

OVERSEERS

PASTORS

PREACHERS

SERVANTS OF GOD

SHEPHERDS

SOLDIERS OF CHRIST

STEWARDS OF GOD

TEACHERS

WATCHMEN

WITNESSES

WORKERS

54

"20 Questions"

Directions: Choose the correct answers to these twenty questions and then find both answers in the puzzle on the next page.

1. Which prophet gave instructions for healing to a leprous Syrian army captain?   (a)Elisha   (b)Elijah

2. Which man was the king of the southern kingdom of Judah?   (a)Rehoboam   (b)Jeroboam

3. Samson was a _____.   (a)Nazirite   (b)Nazarene

4. Which man was sent to rebuild the ruined city walls of Jerusalem?   (a)Ezra   (b)Nehemiah

5. Which king of Babylon saw the finger of God write a gloomy, fateful message on a wall?   (a)Belshazzar   (b)Belteshazzar

6. Which man was struck dead by God because he accidently held the Ark of God?   (a)Uzziah   (b)Uzzah

7. Which minor prophet foretold of Christ's betrayal of thirty pieces of silver?   (a)Zephaniah   (b)Zechariah

8. Where did Abram and Sarai live before they left for Canaan?   (a)Ur   (b)Uz

9. Upon which mountain did half the tribes of Israel stand on to pronounce blessings of obedience to the Law?   (a)Gerizim   (b)Ebal

10. Which event occurred first?   (a)The Flood   (b)Tower of Babel

11. Which angel brought glad news to Mary concerning the birth of her first-born son?   (a)Michael   (b)Gabriel

12. Which Gospel was written by the "beloved physician?"   (a)John   (b)Luke

13. Which man and his wife died because they lied unto the Holy Ghost?   (a)Ananias   (b)Aquila

14. Which church did the Lord describe as being lukewarm?   (a)Thyatira   (b)Laodicea

15. Paul received the Macedonian vision from which city?   (a)Tarsus   (b)Troas

16. Who was the runaway slave that was converted and then sent back to his master by the apostle Paul? (a)Onesimus (b)Onesiphorus

17. Who was the thief that the Jews wanted released rather than Christ? (a)Barnabas (b)Barabbas

18. Christ ascended back to heaven from Mount _____. (a)Moriah (b)Olivet

19. What New Testament book mentions the way of Cain, the error of Balaam, and the gainsaying of Korah? (a)Jude (b)Titus

20. Who was the early church leader that was persuaded by a vision to preach to a Gentile centurion and his family? (a)Peter (b)Philip

ANANIAS	GABRIEL	NAZARITE	THYATIRA
AQUILA	GERIZIM	NEHEMIAH	TITUS
BARABBAS	JEROBOAM	OLIVET	TOWER OF BABEL
BARNABAS	JOHN	ONESIMUS	TROAS
BELSHAZZAR	JUDE	ONESIPHORUS	UR
BELTESHAZZAR	LAODICEA	PETER	UZ
EBAL	LUKE	PHILIP	UZZAH
ELIJAH	MICHAEL	REHOBOAM	UZZIAH
ELISHA	MORIAH	TARSUS	ZECHARIAH
EZRA	NAZARENE	THE FLOOD	ZEPHANIAH

```
U K L E L E A H C I M H T S U S R A T U
S R B R S L A A L I U Q A H T A R G S S
E A E E U I T N E Q H H A Z Y A S A A U
L R L J M S S A A C A J H E Z A R B B T
O T S E I H U N T I I T M Z L U T R B I
J O H N S A R I R L M D A E D U J I A T
N E A E E E O A E R E H O B O A M E R S
N A Z R N H H S E L S D B A M A O L A A
G Z Z H O C P T H E F L O O L B R B B R
H E A A E I I E T O W E R O F B A B E L
A A R Z R R S L E J W I E L L N H T S A
E Z I I A E E I V T A O J F R F E A A H
E L Z Z Z B N J I H A I N A H P E Z O C
N Z A I Z I O E L A R A B L U K E H R I
U N A H H U M H O I P P I L I H P U T M
```

55

Famous Trios

```
D I L D A D S E N A R F T D H D
A E Y R A M L U N D A R E T O A
H L M D M I R A I D N A U L F G
S I L E P N H O J A O R R E I O
U I G H T E T S O H G Y L O H X
B A A A R R T M H S E S H A N A
O Z S P E U I R M A N N O J R L
P H E P P S T U E M D O R P A H
S T H I M O S E S P E R S Z Z M
E E E R E L E Z H M B U A A A I
S H M G Z O P H A R A R J C L R
S P A A S M E R C T U S E J H I
O A J H J O T T H S U T S E F A
M J E P T H E H A S H A U U S M
I M I M A P R O M E J U S T I S
```

Connect each member of a Bible trio with a line.

AGRIPPA	AARON	ABEDNEGO
ELIPHAZ	DIOTREPHES	BILDAD
GOD	FELIX	DEMETRIUS
GAIUS	HAM	FESTUS
MARY	JAMES	HOLY GHOST
MOSES	JESUS	JAPHETH
NAOMI	MARTHA	JOHN
PETER	MESHACH	LAZARUS
SHADRACH	RUTH	MIRIAM
SHEM	ZOPHAR	ORPAH

56

Seals, Trumpets, and Vials

```
E A E S O B I B L A C K H O R S E
U E N W E M I S L A I V N E E S O
P S A O R A M T A R E D M A R D S
H R P B I R T N T W S O T O I E N
R O S O H T R O H E R E H A V A O
A H T I T Y A I B S R D V F E T I
T E E L L R T T T L E W A E V H T
E L P S I E D A E R O M A I N A C
S A M R H D R A O G I O R T R S U
D P U O E S P R N N E R D N E C R
R P R R F O E S E V T V I A M R T
I S T A N U I M T T A S L I Y S S
E A L T Q L E W H O R S U V S U E
S L H N E S N G I R O U Q C U C D
U R O N R I V E R S T O B L O O D
P C C O O D L F D O O H A I L L A
R E H A D A R K N E S S E S S E B
R O H T O D E V O M E R T H G I L
```

BITTER WATERS	HEAT	SEA TO BLOOD
BLACK HORSE	HORSEMEN	SEVEN
BOILS	LIGHT REMOVED	SILENCE
CONQUEROR	LOCUST	STARS FALL
DARKNESS	MARTYRED SOULS	TRUMPETS
DEATH	ONE THIRD	VEGETATION
DESTRUCTION	PALE HORSE	VIALS
EUPHRATES DRIES UP	RED HORSE	WAR
FAMINE	RIVERS TO BLOOD	WHITE HORSE
HAIL	SEALS	

Answers

1 The Books of the Old Testament

2 Old Testament Themes

3 The Creation Story

4 Animals of the Bible

5 Fowls of the Air

6 Insects and Reptiles

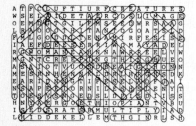

7 Trees in the Bible

8 Land Divisions in Palestine

9 Bible Deserts and Wilderness

10 "A" Words

11 "J" Words

12 Women of the Bible

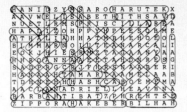

13 Famous Couples

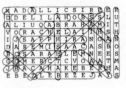

ABRAHAM
ADAM
AHAB
ANANIAS
AQUILA
BOAZ
DAVID
HOSEA
ISAAC
JACOB
JOSEPH
SAMSON
ZACHARIAS

BATHSHEBA
DELILAH
ELISABETH
EVE
GOMER
JEZEBEL
MARY
PRISCILLA
RACHEL
REBEKAH
RUTH
SAPPHIRA
SARAH

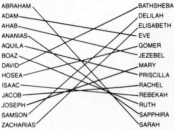

14 The Wanderings of Israel

15 Sacrifices and Offerings

16 The Mountains of Palestine

17 Palestinian Valleys

18 The Judges of Israel

19 Kings of Israel

20 Kings of Judah

21 Kings and Their Domains

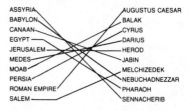

ASSYRIA
BABYLON
CANAAN
EGYPT
JERUSALEM
MEDES
MOAB
PERSIA
ROMAN EMPIRE
SALEM

AUGUSTUS CAESAR
BALAK
CYRUS
DARIUS
HEROD
JABIN
MELCHIZEDEK
NEBUCHADNEZZAR
PHARAOH
SENNACHERIB

22 Israel's Enemies

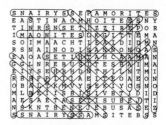

23 People from Proverbs

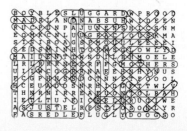

24 God Is

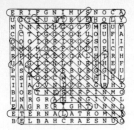

25 Names and Titles of the Devil

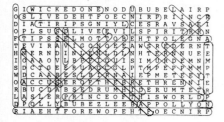

26 Prophets and Prophetesses

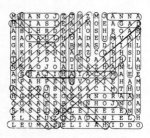

27 Marks of Famous Men

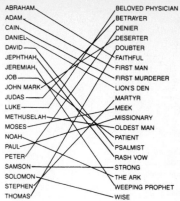

Matching exercise:

ABRAHAM	BELOVED PHYSICIAN
ADAM	BETRAYER
CAIN	DENIER
DANIEL	DESERTER
DAVID	DOUBTER
JEPHTHAH	FAITHFUL
JEREMIAH	FIRST MAN
JOB	FIRST MURDERER
JOHN MARK	LION'S DEN
JUDAS	MARTYR
LUKE	MEEK
METHUSELAH	MISSIONARY
MOSES	OLDEST MAN
NOAH	PATIENT
PAUL	PSALMIST
PETER	RASH VOW
SAMSON	STRONG
SOLOMON	THE ARK
STEPHEN	WEEPING PROPHET
THOMAS	WISE

28 Bible Doctrines

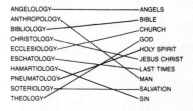

Matching exercise:

ANGELOLOGY	ANGELS
ANTHROPOLOGY	BIBLE
BIBLIOLOGY	CHURCH
CHRISTOLOGY	GOD
ECCLESIOLOGY	HOLY SPIRIT
ESCHATOLOGY	JESUS CHRIST
HAMARTIOLOGY	LAST TIMES
PNEUMATOLOGY	MAN
SOTERIOLOGY	SALVATION
THEOLOGY	SIN

29 Bible Authors

30 Famous Duets

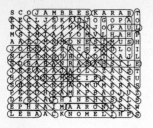

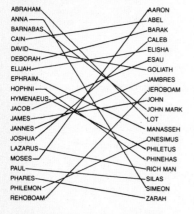

ABRAHAM	AARON
ANNA	ABEL
BARNABAS	BARAK
CAIN	CALEB
DAVID	ELISHA
DEBORAH	ESAU
ELIJAH	GOLIATH
EPHRAIM	JAMBRES
HOPHNI	JEROBOAM
HYMENAEUS	JOHN
JACOB	JOHN MARK
JAMES	LOT
JANNES	MANASSEH
JOSHUA	ONESIMUS
LAZARUS	PHILETUS
MOSES	PHINEHAS
PAUL	RICH MAN
PHARES	SILAS
PHILEMON	SIMEON
REHOBOAM	ZARAH

31 More People from Proverbs

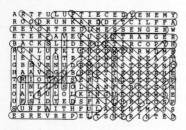

32 The Books of the New Testament

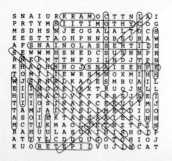

33 Biblical Occupations

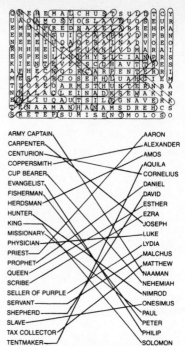

ARMY CAPTAIN	AARON
CARPENTER	ALEXANDER
CENTURION	AMOS
COPPERSMITH	AQUILA
CUP BEARER	CORNELIUS
EVANGELIST	DANIEL
FISHERMAN	DAVID
HERDSMAN	ESTHER
HUNTER	EZRA
KING	JOSEPH
MISSIONARY	LUKE
PHYSICIAN	LYDIA
PRIEST	MALCHUS
PROPHET	MATTHEW
QUEEN	NAAMAN
SCRIBE	NEHEMIAH
SELLER OF PURPLE	NIMROD
SERVANT	ONESIMUS
SHEPHERD	PAUL
SLAVE	PETER
TAX COLLECTOR	PHILIP
TENTMAKER	SOLOMON

34 Themes of New Testament Books

74

35 The Christmas Story

THE BIRTHDAY OF CHRIST

36 Genealogy of Jesus (Matthew 1)

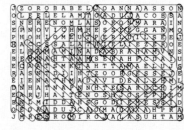

37 Genealogy of Jesus (Luke 3)

38 The Parables of Christ

39 Two-Word Titles

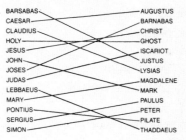

BARSABAS — AUGUSTUS
CAESAR — BARNABAS
CLAUDIUS — CHRIST
HOLY — GHOST
JESUS — ISCARIOT
JOHN — JUSTUS
JOSES — LYSIAS
JUDAS — MAGDALENE
LEBBAEUS — MARK
MARY — PAULUS
PONTIUS — PETER
SERGIUS — PILATE
SIMON — THADDAEUS

40 Words and Their Biblical Definitions

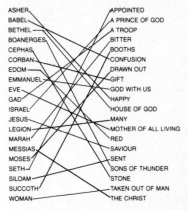

ASHER — APPOINTED
BABEL — A PRINCE OF GOD
BETHEL — A TROOP
BOANERGES — BITTER
CEPHAS — BOOTHS
CORBAN — CONFUSION
EDOM — DRAWN OUT
EMMANUEL — GIFT
EVE — GOD WITH US
GAD — HAPPY
ISRAEL — HOUSE OF GOD
JESUS — MANY
LEGION — MOTHER OF ALL LIVING
MARAH — RED
MESSIAS — SAVIOUR
MOSES — SENT
SETH — SONS OF THUNDER
SILOAM — STONE
SUCCOTH — TAKEN OUT OF MAN
WOMAN — THE CHRIST

41 Who Was Spoken To?

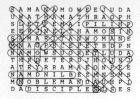

1. JOHN
2. NATHANAEL
3. MARY
4. NICODEMUS
5. SAMARITAN WOMAN
6. NOBLE MAN
7. IMPOTENT MAN
8. PHILIP
9. JESUS
10. ADULTEROUS WOMAN
11. BLIND MAN
12. JEWS
13. MARTHA
14. LAZARUS
15. JUDAS
16. DISCIPLES
17. GOD
18. PILATE
19. THOMAS
20. PETER

42 The Crucifixion

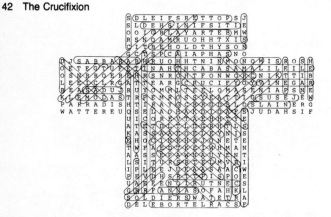

43 Names and Titles of Christ

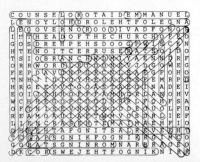

44 Names and Titles of the Holy Spirit

45 Places of Paul's Travels

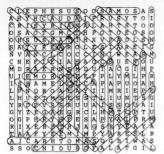

46 Who Said It?

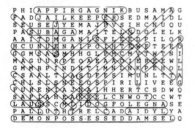

1. LUKE
2. CHRIST
3. PETER
4. GAMALIEL
5. THE TWELVE
6. STEPHEN
7. SIMON
8. ETHIOPIAN EUNUCH
9. PHILIP
10. SAUL
11. ANANIAS
12. CORNELIUS
13. JAMES
14. MAN OF MACEDONIA
15. LYDIA
16. DEMON-POSSESSED DAMSEL
17. JAILKEEPER
18. PAUL
19. GALLIO

20. EVIL SPIRIT
21. TOWN CLERK
22. AGABUS
23. FESTUS
24. KING AGRIPPA
25. ANGEL OF GOD

47 "Tion" Words

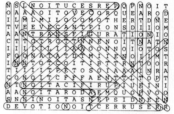

48 More "Tion" Words

49 Names of the Saved

50 Christian Characteristics

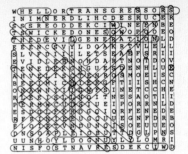

51 The Christian Walk

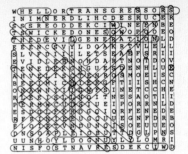

1. BEFORE GOD
2. UPRIGHTLY
3. IN NEWNESS OF LIFE
4. AFTER THE SPIRIT
5. BY FAITH
6. IN THE SPIRIT
7. WORTHY OF THE VOCATION
8. IN LOVE
9. AS CHILDREN OF LIGHT
10. CIRCUMSPECTLY
11. WORTHY OF THE LORD
12. IN HIM
13. IN WISDOM
14. WORTHY OF GOD
15. HONESTLY
16. IN THE LIGHT
17. AFTER HIS COMMANDMENTS
18. IN TRUTH

52 Names of the Wicked

53 Types of Ministers

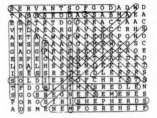

54 "20 Questions"

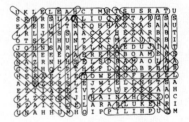

1. a	11. b
2. a	12. b
3. a	13. a
4. b	14. b
5. a	15. b
6. b	16. a
7. b	17. b
8. a	18. b
9. a	19. a
10. a	20. a

55 Famous Trios

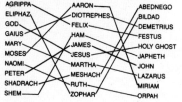

AGRIPPA
ELIPHAZ
GOD
GAIUS
MARY
MOSES
NAOMI
PETER
SHADRACH
SHEM

AARON
DIOTREPHES
FELIX
HAM
JAMES
JESUS
MARTHA
MESHACH
RUTH
ZOPHAR

ABEDNEGO
BILDAD
DEMETRIUS
FESTUS
HOLY GHOST
JAPHETH
JOHN
LAZARUS
MIRIAM
ORPAH

56 Seals, Trumpets, and Vials

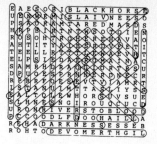